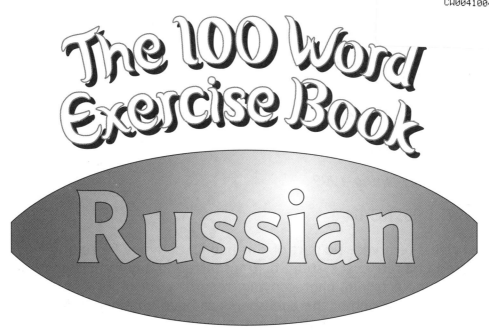

The 100 Word Exercise Book

Russian

Series concept: Jane Wightwick
Russian edition: Helena Chick

Published by *GW Publishing*
47a High Street
Chinnor
Oxfordshire OX9 4DJ

First published 1999

© *GW Publishing 1999*

ISBN 1-903103-04-5

Designed by: Robert Bowers

Illustrated by: Mahmoud Gaafar

Printed in Hong Kong
by Wing King Tong Co. Ltd.

◎ CONTENTS

INTRODUCTION

In this activity book you'll find 100 key words for you to learn to read in Russian. All of the activities are designed specifically for reading non-Latin script languages. Many of the activities are inspired by the kind of games used to teach children to read their own language: flashcards, matching games, memory games, joining exercises, etc. This is not only a more effective method of learning to read a new script, but also much more fun.

We've included a **Scriptbreaker** to get you started. This is a friendly introduction to the Russian script that will give you tips on how to remember the letters.

Then you can move on to the 8 **Topics**. Each topic presents essential words in large type. There is also a pronunciation guide so you know how to say the words. These words are also featured in the tear-out **Flashcard** section at the back of the book. When you've mastered the words, you can go on to try out the activities and games for that topic.

There's also a **Round-up** section to review all your new words and the **Answers** to all the activities to check yourself.

Follow this 4-step plan for maximum success:

1 Have a look at the key topic words with their pictures. Then tear out the flashcards and shuffle them. Put them Russian side up. Try to remember what the word means and turn the card over to check with the English. When you can do this, cover the pronunciation and try to say the word and remember the meaning by looking at the Russian script only.

2 Put the cards English side up and try to say the Russian word. Try the cards again each day both ways around. (When you can remember a card for 7 days in a row, you can file it!)

3 Try out the activities and games for each topic. This will reinforce your recognition of the key words.

4 After you have covered all the topics, you can try the activities in the Round-up section to test your knowledge of all the Russian words in the book. You can also try shuffling all the flashcards together to see how many you can remember.

This flexible and fun way of reading your first words in Russian should give you a head start whether you're learning at home or in a group.

◎ SCRIPTBREAKER

The purpose of this Scriptbreaker is to introduce you to the Russian script and how it is formed. You should not try to memorize the alphabet at this stage, nor try to write the letters yourself. Instead, have a quick look through this section and then move on to the topics, glancing back if you want to work out the letters in a particular word. Remember, though, that recognizing the whole shape of the word in an unfamiliar script is just as important as knowing how it is made up. Using this method you will have a much more instinctive recall of vocabulary and will gain the confidence to expand your knowledge in other directions.

The Russian script — more properly called the Cyrillic script — is not nearly as difficult as it might seem at first glance. There are many letters that are the same as the English ones, there are capital letters, and, unlike English, words are usually spelled as they sound:

- Russian spelling and pronunciation are much more systematic than in English
- You will recognize some of the letters straight away, but beware of false friends!

◎ The alphabet

There are 32 letters in the Cyrillic alphabet. A good way of learning the alphabet is to take it in two stages.

Stage 1

The first stage consists of twenty relatively "easy" letters.

Six of these letters closely resemble their English equivalents. These are:

а *(a)*	е/ё *(ye/yo)*	К *(k)*
М *(m)*	О *(o or a)*	Т *(t)*

Five are misleading because they resemble English letters but are not equivalents:

В *(v)*	Н *(n)*	р *(r)*
С *(s)*	у *(oo)*	

We can now use these letters to make some words:

там *(tam)*	нос *(nos)*
рука *(rooka)*	утка *(ootka)*

The remaining nine letters are less familar shapes:

б *(b)*	Г *(g)*	Д *(d)*
З *(z)*	И *(ee)*	Й *(y)*
Л *(l)*	П *(p)*	ф *(f)*

We can use these letters to make some more words:

СТУЛ *(stool)*   СПИНА *(speena)*
ПЛИТА *(pleeta)*   ГДЕ *(gdye)*

✔ Russian has 32 letters
✔ Some letters are like their English equivalents
✔ Some letters look like their English equivalents, but are **false friends**

Stage 2

Stage two consists of the final 12 letters; all of these are again less familiar shapes.

The following six letters are individual letters in Russian, where in English a similar sound is made by putting two or more letters together:

Ж *(zh)*   Х *(kh)*   Ц *(ts)*
Ч *(ch)*   Ш *(sh)*   Щ *(shch)*

✔ There are five false friends

В = *v*   Н = *n*   р = *r*
С = *s*   У = *oo*

Now look at these words:

ШКАФ *(shkaf)*   ШКОЛА *(shkola)*
ХОЛМ *(kholm)*   ЖИВОТ *(zheevot)*

The next four letters are all vowels:

Ы *(i)*   Э *(e)*
Ю *(yoo)*   Я *(ya)*

The final two letters, although part of the Cyrillic alphabet, can more easily be thought of as "signs" than as letters. Indeed, they are called the "hard sign" and the "soft sign". They do not really have a sound value, but rather affect the letters that precede or follow them.

Ъ *(hard sign)*   Ь *(soft sign)*

Now look at these words:

рыба *(riba)*   дверь *(dvyer')*

чистый *(cheestiy)*   туфля *(tooflya)*

◎ Pronunciation tips

This exercise book has simplified some aspects of pronunciation in order to emphasize the basics. Don't worry at this stage about being precisely correct —the other letters in a word will help you to be understood.

Many Russian letters are pronounced in a similar way to their English equivalents, but here are a few which need special attention:

е and ё	although they are pronounced quite differently (*ye* and *yo*), these letters are considered to form a single letter of the Russian alphabet. In Russian books the two dots in ё are often omitted.
о	often pronounced as "*a*". This happens when "*o*" is in an unstressed position in the word
х	pronounced like the "*ch*" in the Scottish "*loch*"
щ	pronounced like "sh" followed by "ch", as in "pushchair"
ы	a tricky sound; try saying the "ea" as in "tea" and then, with the mouth in the same position, try saying "oo" as in "boot"
р	pronounced rolled at the front of the mouth
й	this letter occurs mainly after vowels, forming diphthongs, and is like the "y" in "boy"
ь	the "soft sign" is most commonly found at the end of the word, or is followed by a consonant. In these two cases it is not pronounced at all, but indicates that the preceding consonant is "soft" in sound. When the "soft sign" precedes a vowel, it is pronounced like "y" in "yet"
ъ	the "hard sign" does not occur often. It always precedes a vowel and is pronounced like "y" in "yet"; it also makes the preceding consonant "hard" in sound

This book also includes underlining to show you which part of the word is stressed (pronounced with more emphasis). Remember, though, that the guidelines are only approximate and that you will find natural pronunciation sometimes deviates from these rules.

- ✔ Many Russian letters are pronounced in a similar way to English
- ✔ Russian spelling is much more straightforward than that of English
- ✔ You will often hear see "o" written, but hear it pronounced "a"

Summary of the Russian/Cyrillic alphabet

The table below shows all the Russian letters, both capitals and lower case. Hopefully, you will already recognize some of them, and as you move through the topics, they will become more familiar to you.

А	а	*a*	И	и	*ee*	С	с	*s*	Ъ ъ	*hard sign*
Б	б	*b*	Й	й	*y*	Т	т	*t*		
В	в	*v*	К	к	*k*	У	у	*oo*	Ы ы	*i*
Г	г	*g*	Л	л	*l*	Ф	ф	*f*	Ь ь	*soft sign*
Д	д	*d*	М	м	*m*	Х	х	*kh*		
Е	е	*ye*	Н	н	*n*	Ц	ц	*ts*	Э э	*e*
Ё	ё	*yo*	О	о	*o*	Ч	ч	*chy*	Ю ю	*yoo*
Ж	ж	*zh*	П	п	*p*	Ш	ш	*sh*	Я я	*ya*
З	з	*z*	Р	р	*r*	Щ	щ	*shch*		

① AROUND THE HOME

Look at the pictures of things you might find in a house.
Tear out the flashcards for this topic.
Follow steps 1 and 2 of the plan in the introduction.

стол
stol

телевизор
*tele**vee**zar*

окно
*ak**no***

стул
stool

компьютер
*kam**pyoo**ter*

телефон
*tele**fon***

софа *so**fa***

кровать *kra**vat'***

холодильник
*khala**deel'**neek*

шкаф
shkaf

дверь
dvyer'

плита
*p**lee**ta*

9

◎ **M**atch the pictures with the words, as in the example.

софа

кровать

окно

стол

телевизор

компьютер

телефон

стул

◎ **N**ow match the Russian household words to the English.

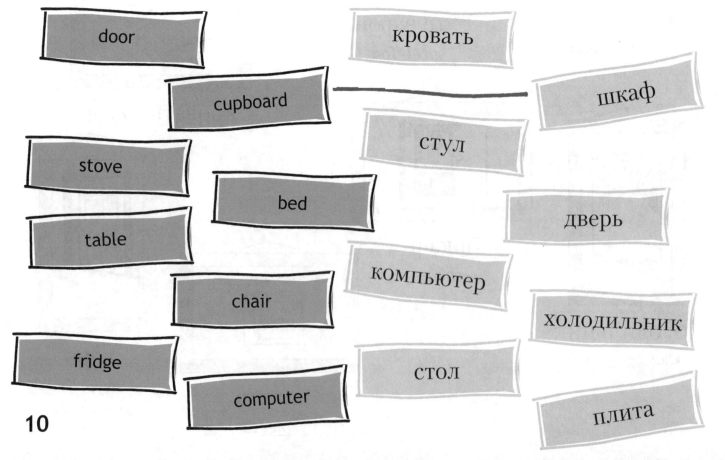

Match the words and their pronunciation.

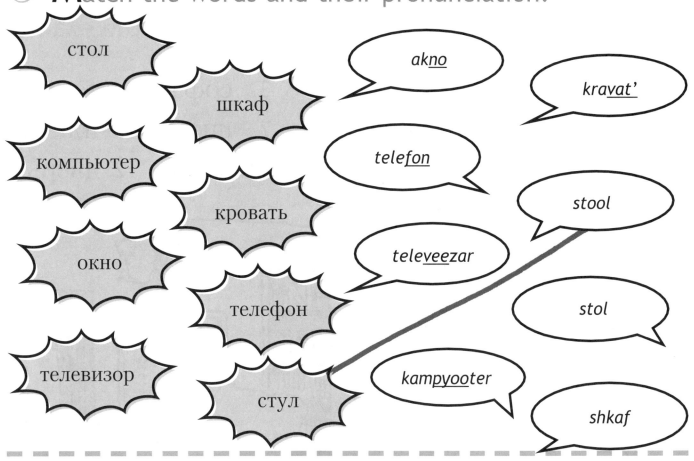

стол

шкаф

akno

kravat'

компьютер

кровать

telefon

stool

окно

телефон

televeezar

stol

телевизор

стул

kampyooter

shkaf

See if you can find these words in the word square.

The words can run left to right, or top to bottom:

плита	п	т	д	т	о	л	с	п
кровать	т	к	р	о	в	а	т	ь
стул	в	с	л	ь	п	у	у	в
стол	л	с	т	о	л	ф	л	о
дверь	д	а	д	в	е	р	ь	с
софа	т	ь	т	о	ь	л	х	о
	п	л	и	т	а	д	н	ф
	к	и	о	в	а	п	е	а

Decide where the household items should go. Then write the correct number in the picture, as in the example.

1. стол
2. стул
3. софа
4. телевизор
5. телефон
6. кровать
7. шкаф
8. плита
9. холодильник
10. компьютер
11. окно
12. дверь

Now see if you can fill in the household word at the bottom of the page by choosing the correct Russian.

стол ⓒ   стул ⓑ   кровать ⓦ

софа ⓘ   кровать ⓐ   телевизор ⓕ

компьютер ⓓ   телевизор ⓝ   дверь ⓘ

стул ⓑ   стол ⓓ   холодильник ⓚ

софа ⓢ   телефон ⓣ   окно ⓞ

дверь ⓖ   шкаф ⓦ   стул ⓔ

English word: ⓦ ◯ ◯ ◯ ◯ ◯

❷ CLOTHES

Look at the pictures of different clothes.
Tear out the flashcards for this topic.
Follow steps 1 and 2 of the plan in the introduction.

ремень
remyen'

пуловер
poolover

брюки
bryookee

шорты
shorti

носок
nasok

футболка
footbolka

пальто
pal'to

юбка
yoopka

платье
plat'e

шляпа *shlyapa*

туфля *tooflya*

рубашка *roobashka*

Match the Russian words and their pronunciation.

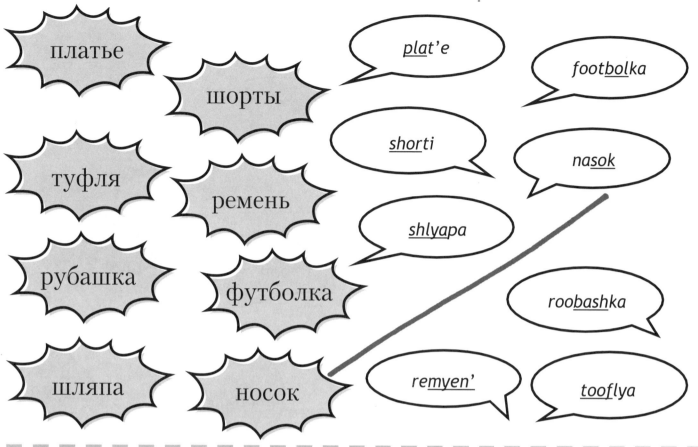

платье

шорты

туфля

ремень

рубашка

футболка

шляпа

носок

plat'e

footbolka

shorti

nasok

shlyapa

roobashka

remyen'

tooflya

See if you can find these clothes in the word square.

The words can run left to right, or top to bottom:

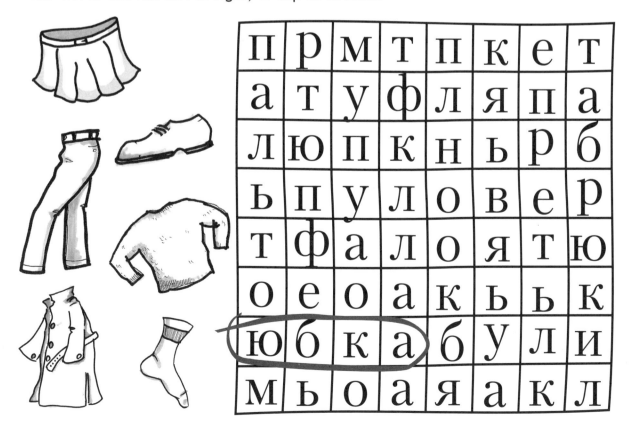

п	р	м	т	п	к	е	т
а	т	у	ф	л	я	п	а
л	ю	п	к	н	ь	р	б
ь	п	у	л	о	в	е	р
т	ф	а	л	о	я	т	ю
о	е	о	а	к	ь	ь	к
ю	б	к	а	б	у	л	и
м	ь	о	а	я	а	к	л

Now match the Russian words, their pronunciation, and the English meaning, as in the example.

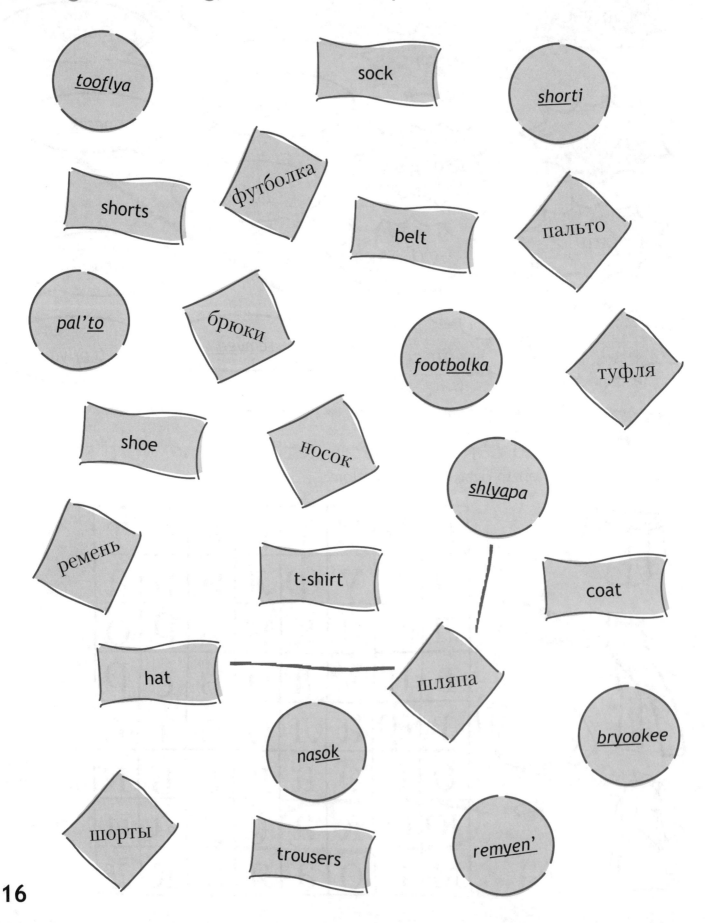

tooflya

sock

shorti

shorts

футболка

belt

пальто

pal'to

брюки

footbolka

туфля

shoe

носок

shlyapa

ремень

t-shirt

coat

hat

шляпа

bryookee

nasok

шорты

trousers

remyen'

Candy is going on holiday. Count how many of each type of clothing she is packing in her suitcase.

шляпа	2	пальто		ремень		туфля	
брюки		шорты		платье		носок	
юбка		футболка		рубашка		пуловер	

Someone has ripped up the Russian words for clothes. Can you join the two halves of the words, as the example?

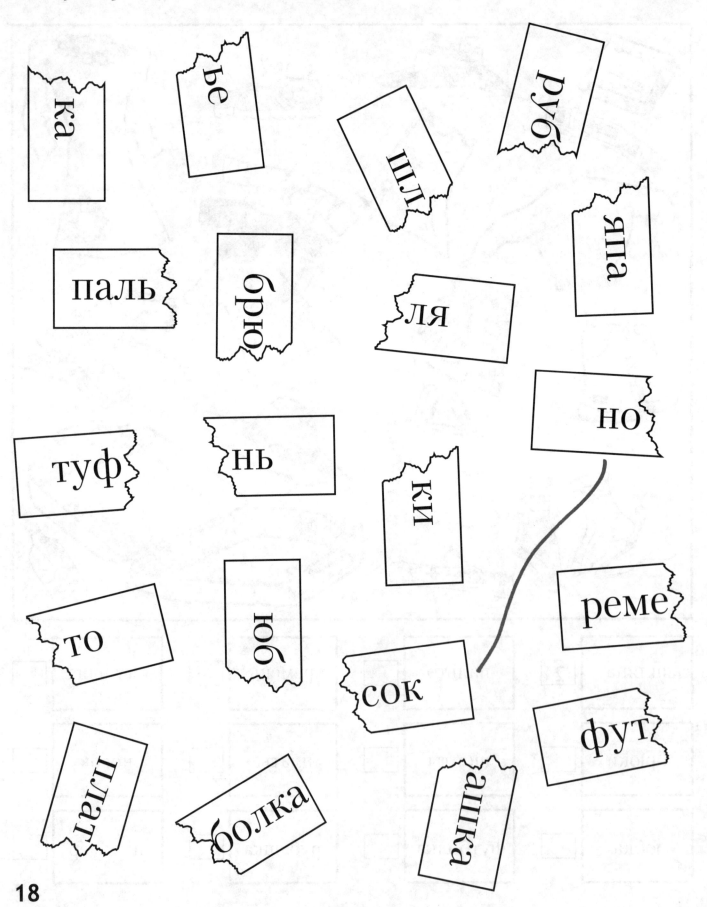

③ AROUND TOWN

Look at the pictures of things you might find around town.
Tear out the flashcards for this topic.
Follow steps 1 and 2 of the plan in the introduction.

гостиница   *gasteeneetsa*

автобус

aftoboos

дом

dom

машина

masheena

кино

keeno

поезд

poyest

такси   *taksee*

велосипед

vyelaseepyet

школа   *shkola*

дорога *daroga*

магазин *magazeen*

ресторан

restaran

Match the Russian words to their English equivalents.

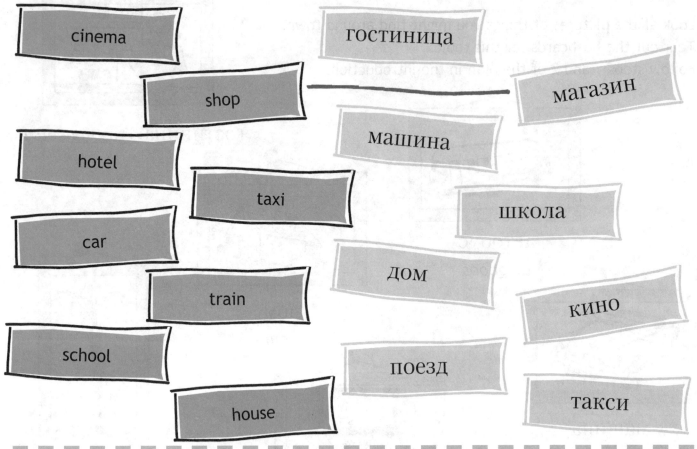

cinema

shop

hotel

taxi

car

train

school

house

гостиница

магазин

машина

школа

дом

кино

поезд

такси

Now list the correct order of the English words to match the Russian word chain, as in the example.

автобус — дом — дорога — велосипед — машина — поезд — такси

bicycle   taxi   house   bus   train   road   car

4 ___ ___ ___ ___ ___ ___

◎ **M**atch the words to the signs.

школа   машина   велосипед   автобус

ресторан   поезд   гостиница   такси

Now choose the Russian word that matches the picture to fill in the English word at the bottom of the page.

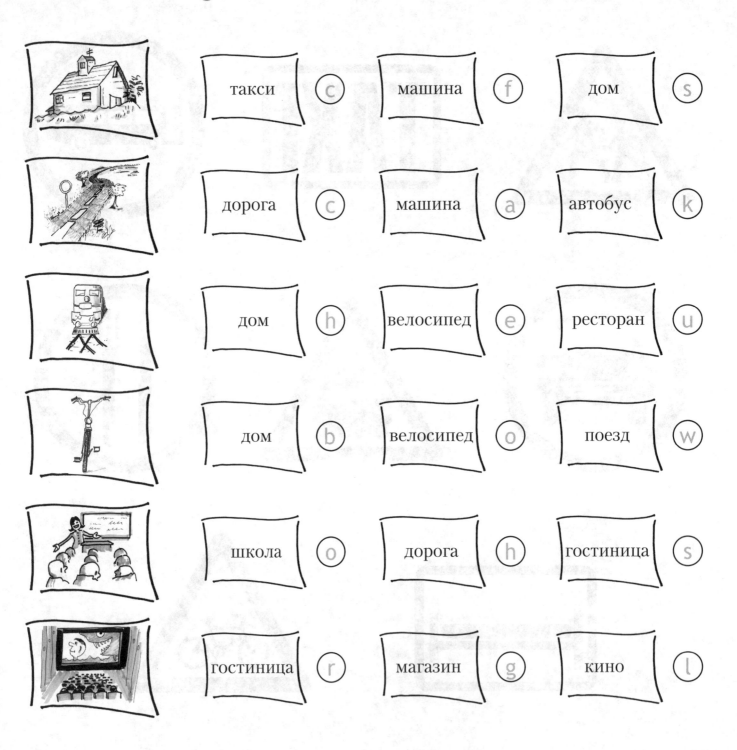

такси ⓒ	машина ⓕ	дом ⓢ
дорога ⓒ	машина ⓐ	автобус ⓚ
дом ⓗ	велосипед ⓔ	ресторан ⓤ
дом ⓑ	велосипед ⓞ	поезд ⓦ
школа ⓞ	дорога ⓗ	гостиница ⓢ
гостиница ⓡ	магазин ⓖ	кино ⓛ

English word: ⓢ ◯ ◯ ◯ ◯ ◯

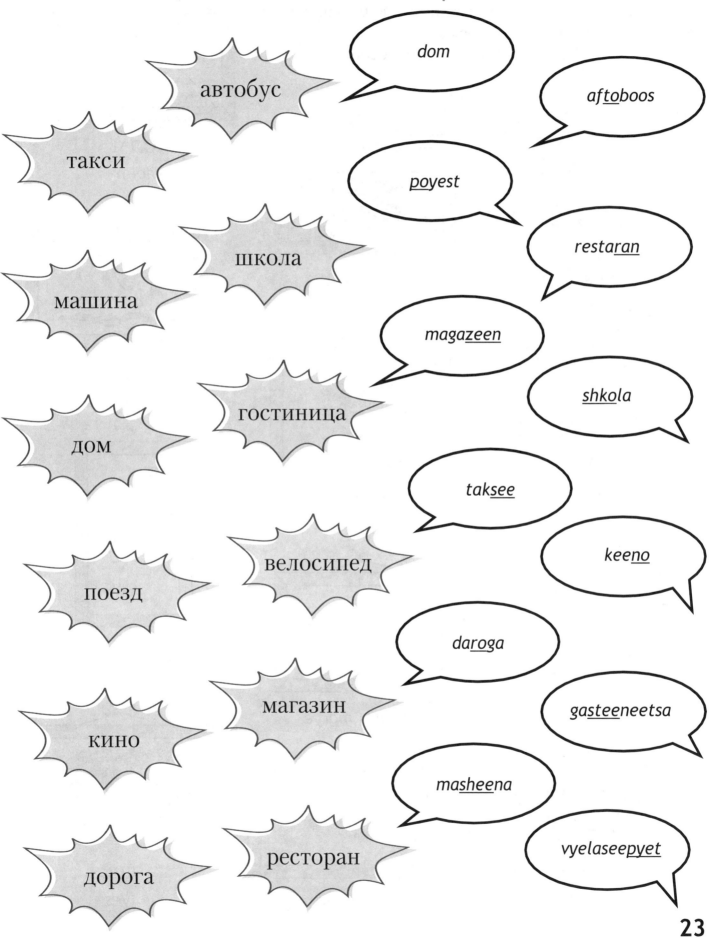

④ COUNTRYSIDE

Look at the pictures of things you might find in the countryside.
Tear out the flashcards for this topic.
Follow steps 1 and 2 of the plan in the introduction.

ХОЛМ
kholm

мост
most

ферма
ferma

озеро
ozera

дерево
dyereva

гора
gara

река *reka*

море *morye*

цветок
tsvetok

поле *polye*

пустыня
poostinya

лес
lyes

24

гора

ферма

море

лес

пустыня

холм

озеро

мост

река

цветок

дерево

поле

◎ **N**ow tick (✔) the features you can find in this landscape.

мост	✔	дерево	☐	пустыня	☐	холм	☐
гора	☐	море	☐	поле	☐	лес	☐
озеро	☐	река	☐	цветок	☐	ферма	☐

Match the Russian words and their pronunciation.

гора

река

лес

пустыня

море

ферма

мост

поле

poostinya

ferma

polye

lyes

reka

most

morye

gara

See if you can find these words in the word square.

The words can run left to right, or top to bottom.

дерево
ферма
холм
цветок
мост
озеро

е	м	м	н	л	ь	о	я
т	х	о	л	м	ы	ф	л
к	я	с	ш	п	о	е	ь
р	т	т	о	з	е	р	о
е	п	ь	л	о	е	м	н
я	а	т	а	ь	ь	а	л
д	е	р	е	в	о	ш	я
е	ь	ц	в	е	т	о	к

27

Finally, test yourself by joining the Russian words, their pronunciation, and the English meanings, as in the example.

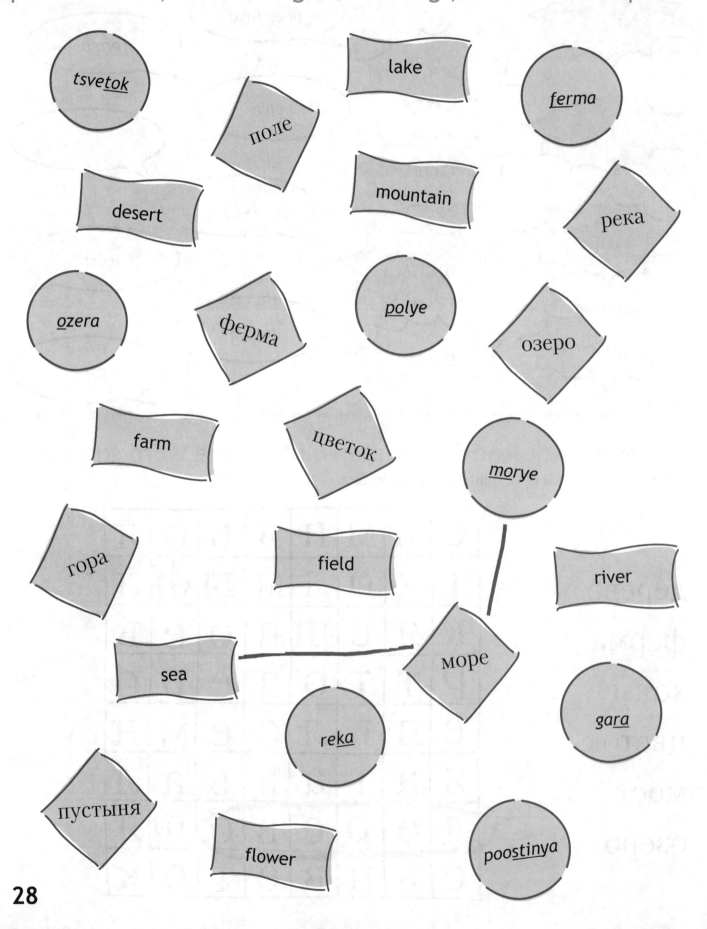

tsvetok

lake

ferma

поле

mountain

desert

река

ozera

ферма

polye

озеро

farm

цветок

morye

гора

field

river

sea

море

gara

reka

пустыня

flower

poostinya

⑤ OPPOSITES

Look at the pictures.
Tear out the flashcards for this topic.
Follow steps 1 and 2 of the plan in the introduction.

грязный

gryazniy

чистый

cheestiy

маленький

malyen'keey

большой

bal'shoy

дешёвый

deshoviy

лёгкий   *lyokhkeey*

медленный   *myedlenniy*

дорогой   *daragoy*

тяжёлый   *teezholiy*

быстрый   *bistriy*

старый   *stariy*

новый   *noviy*

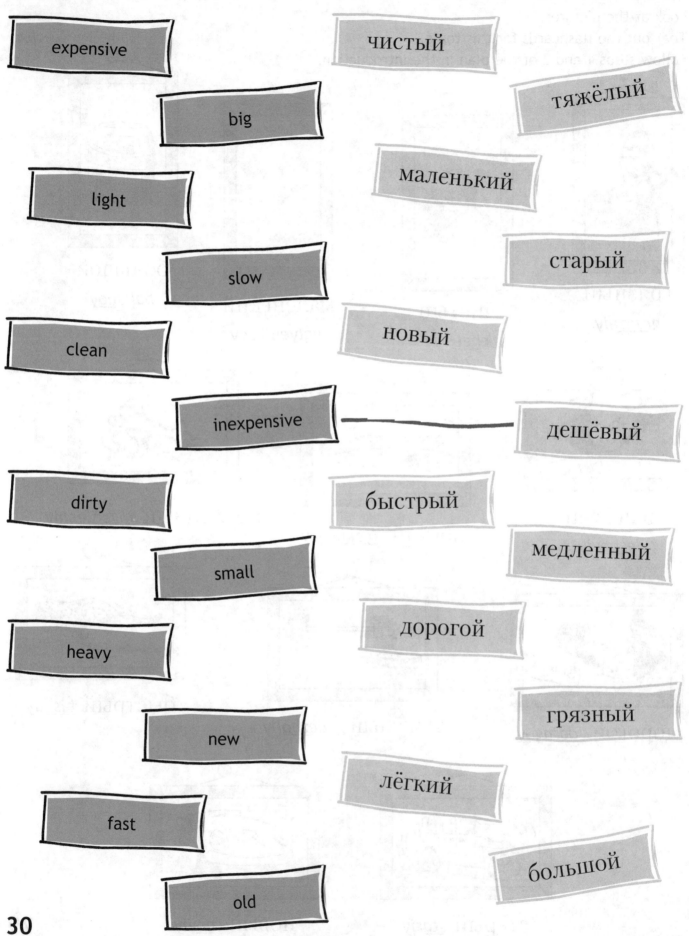

expensive

big

light

slow

clean

inexpensive

dirty

small

heavy

new

fast

old

чистый

тяжёлый

маленький

старый

новый

дешёвый

быстрый

медленный

дорогой

грязный

лёгкий

большой

Now choose the Russian word that matches the picture to fill in the English word at the bottom of the page.

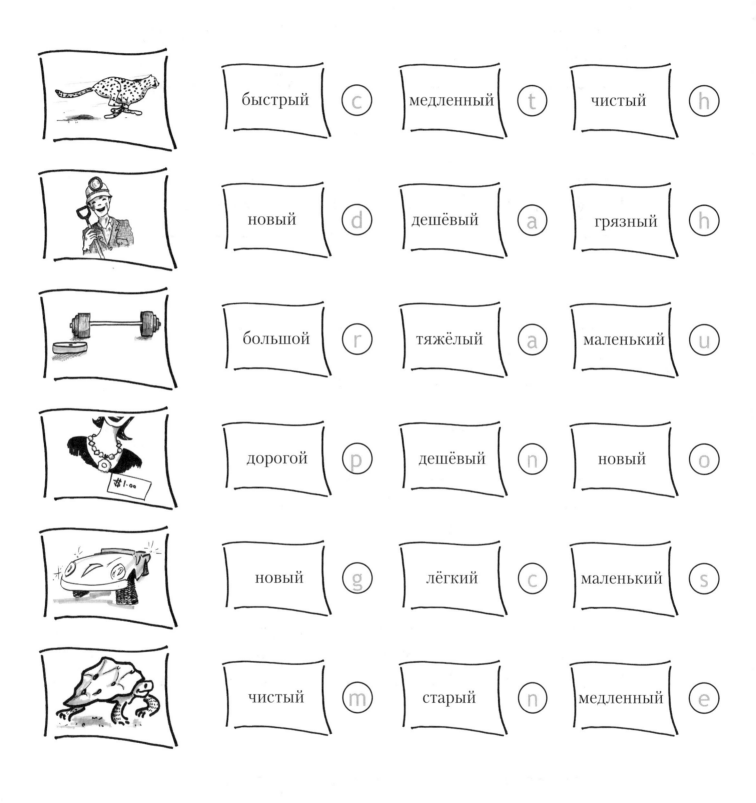

быстрый Ⓒ	медленный Ⓣ	чистый Ⓗ
новый Ⓓ	дешёвый Ⓐ	грязный Ⓗ
большой Ⓡ	тяжёлый Ⓐ	маленький Ⓤ
дорогой Ⓟ	дешёвый Ⓝ	новый Ⓞ
новый Ⓖ	лёгкий Ⓒ	маленький Ⓢ
чистый Ⓜ	старый Ⓝ	медленный Ⓔ

English word: ◯ ◯ ◯ ◯ ◯ ◯

Find the odd one out in these groups of words.

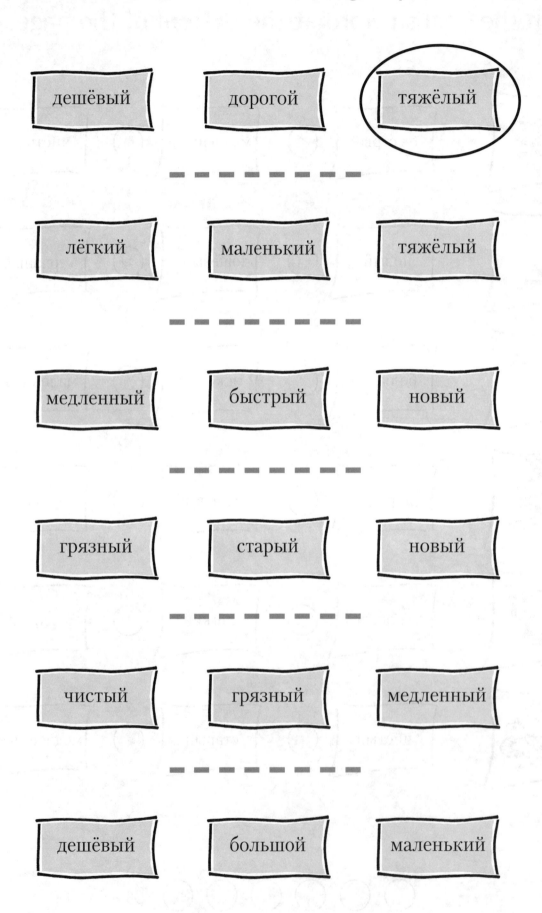

дешёвый   дорогой   тяжёлый

лёгкий   маленький   тяжёлый

медленный   быстрый   новый

грязный   старый   новый

чистый   грязный   медленный

дешёвый   большой   маленький

Finally, join the English words to their Russian opposites, as in the example.

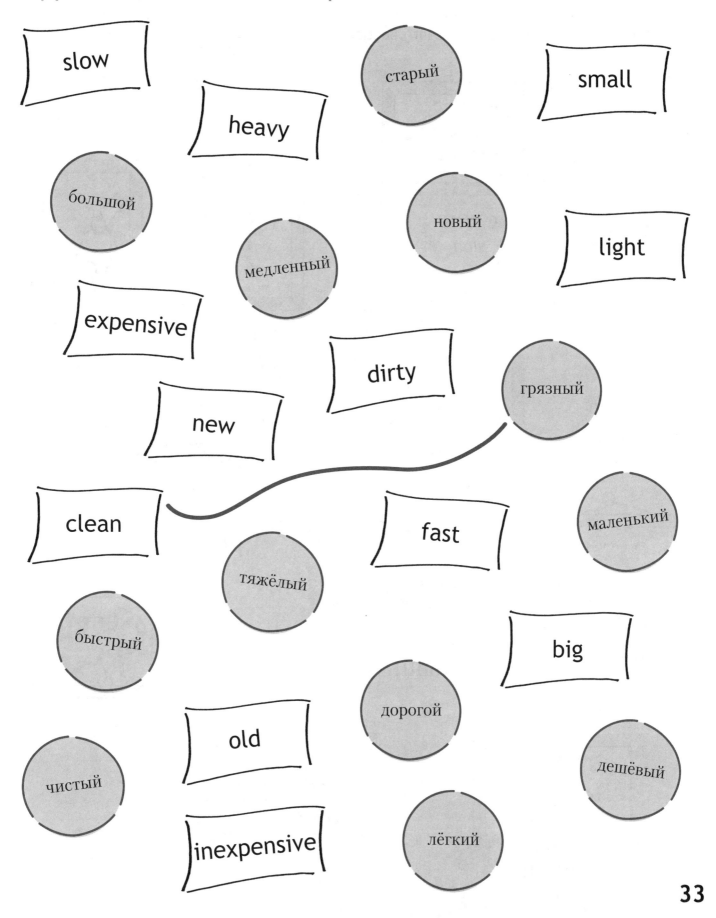

slow

heavy

старый

small

большой

новый

light

медленный

expensive

dirty

грязный

new

clean

fast

маленький

тяжёлый

быстрый

big

дорогой

old

дешёвый

чистый

inexpensive

лёгкий

❻ ANIMALS

Look at the pictures.
Tear out the flashcards for this topic.
Follow steps 1 and 2 of the plan in the introduction.

утка *ootka*

слон
slon

кошка
koshka

собака
sabaka

кролик
kroleek

обезьяна
abes'yana

рыба *riba*

овца *avtsa*

мышь *mish'*

корова *karova*

лошадь
loshat'

лев
lev

34

Match the animals to their associated pictures, as in the example.

кролик

лошадь

обезьяна

кошка

овца

мышь

собака

лев

корова

рыба

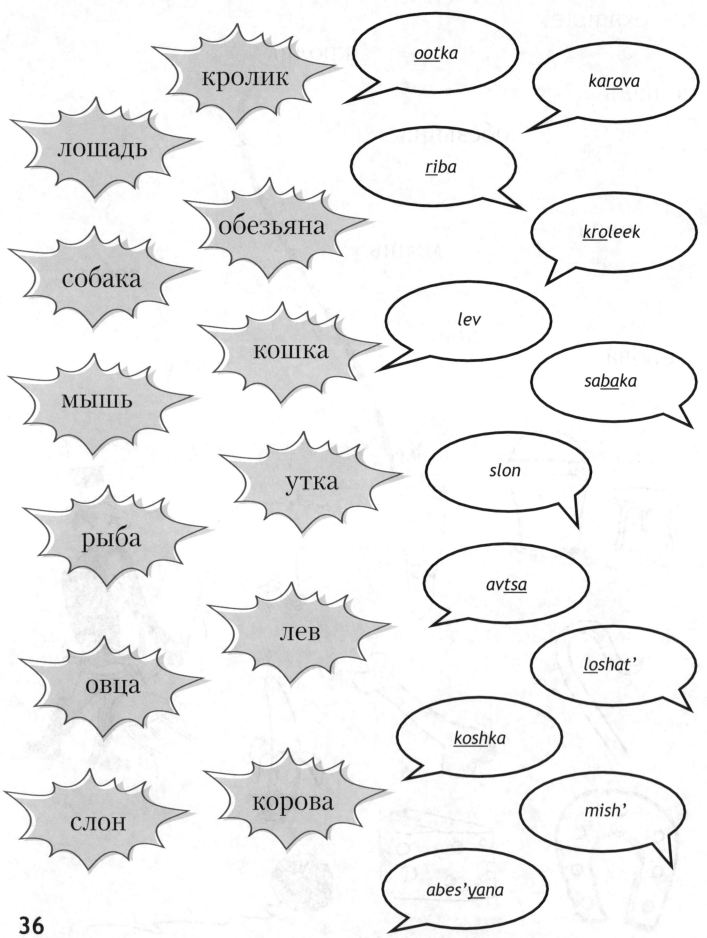

Tick (✔) the animal words you can find in the word pile.

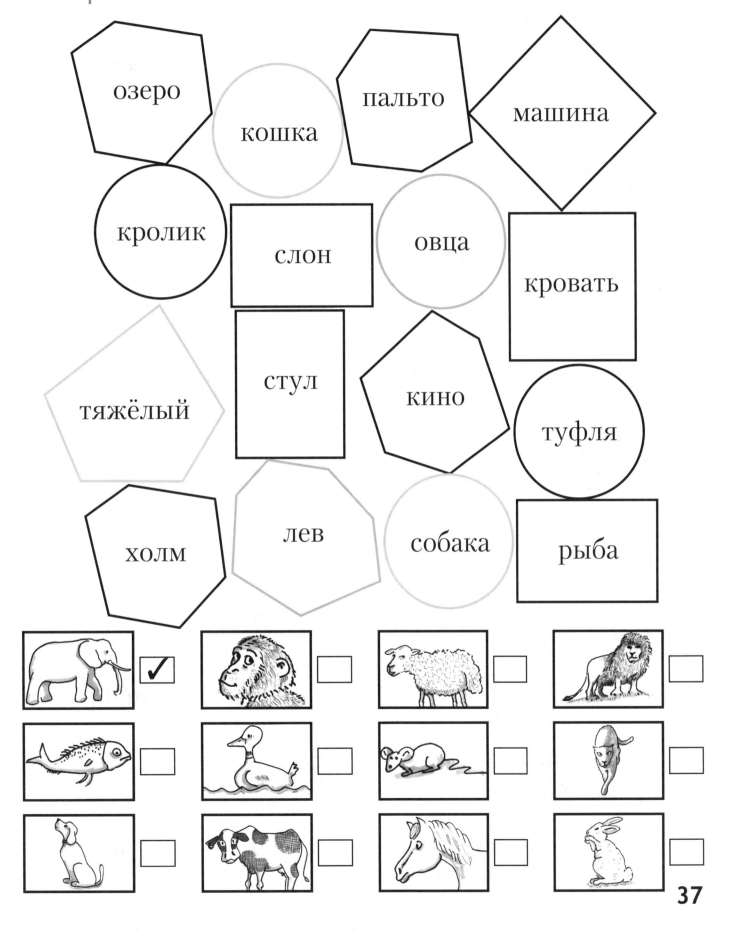

озеро

кошка

пальто

машина

кролик

слон

овца

кровать

тяжёлый

стул

кино

туфля

холм

лев

собака

рыба

37

Join the Russian animals to their English equivalents.

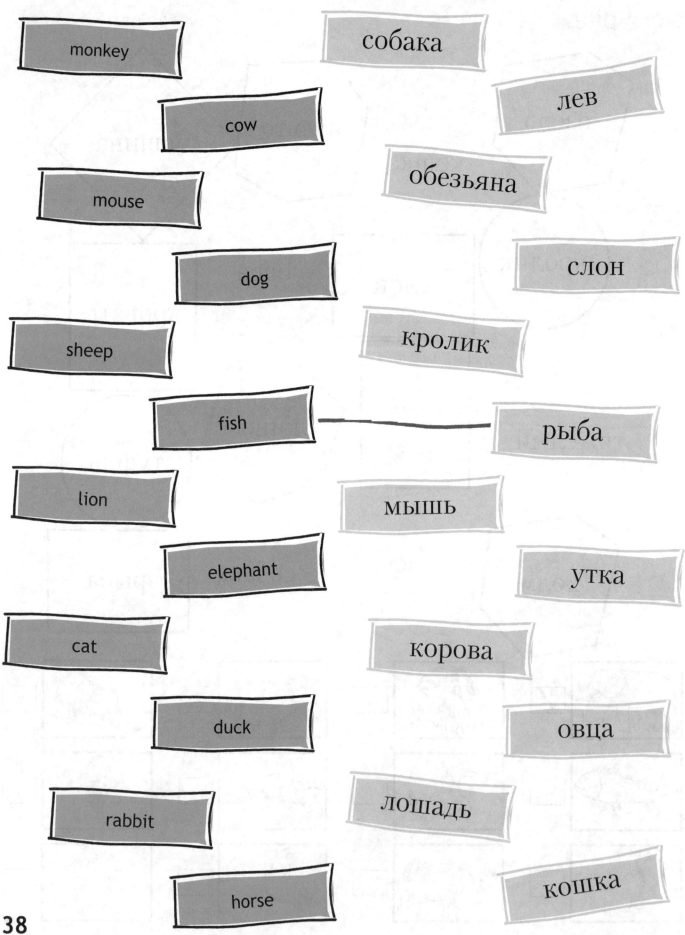

monkey

собака

лев

cow

обезьяна

mouse

слон

dog

кролик

sheep

fish — рыба

lion

мышь

elephant

утка

cat

корова

duck

овца

rabbit

лошадь

horse

кошка

7 PARTS OF THE BODY

Look at the pictures of parts of the body.
Tear out the flashcards for this topic.
Follow steps 1 and 2 of the plan in the introduction.

палец
palets

голова
galava

рука
rooka

глаз *glas*

спина
speena

рука

волосы *volasi*

нога
naga

живот
zheevot

ухо
ookha

нос
nos

рот
rot

Someone has ripped up the Russian words for parts of the body. Can you join the two halves of the word again?

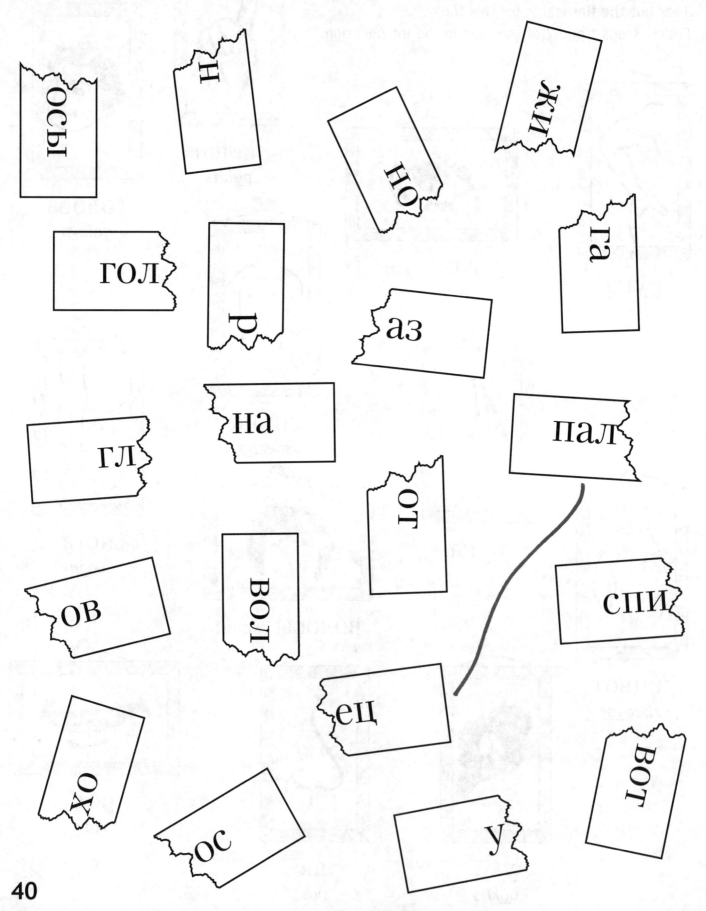

See if you can find and circle six parts of the body in the word square, then draw them in the boxes below.

The words can run left to right, or top to bottom:

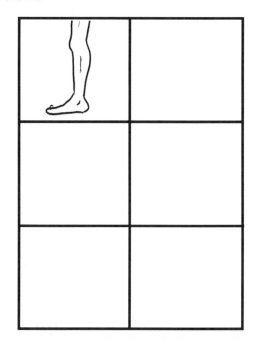

Now match the Russian to the pronunciation.

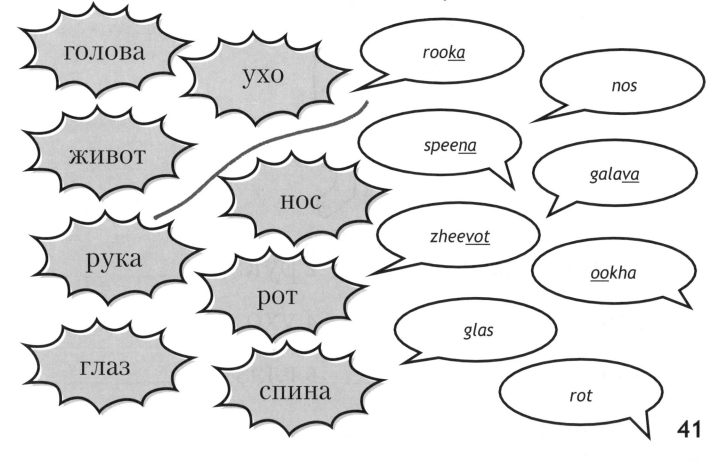

◎ **L**abel the body with the correct number, and write the pronunciation next to the words.

1 живот _zheevot_ _____ 2 рука _____

3 нос _____ 4 ухо _____

5 нога _____ 6 глаз _____

7 палец _____

© **F**inally, match the Russian words, their pronunciation, and the English meanings, as in the example.

8 USEFUL EXPRESSIONS

Look at the pictures.
Tear out the flashcards for this topic.
Follow steps 1 and 2 of the plan in the introduction.

где? *gdye*

нет
nyet

да
da

здравствуйте
zdrastvooytye

до свидания
da sveedaneeya

вчера
fchyera

сегодня
sevodnya

завтра
zaftra

здесь
zdyes'

там *tam*

сейчас *seechas*

сколько стоит?
skol'ka stoeet

извините!
eezveeneetye

отлично!
atleechna

пожалуйста
pazhalsta

спасибо
spaseeba

Match the Russian words to their English equivalents.

Now match the Russian to the pronunciation.

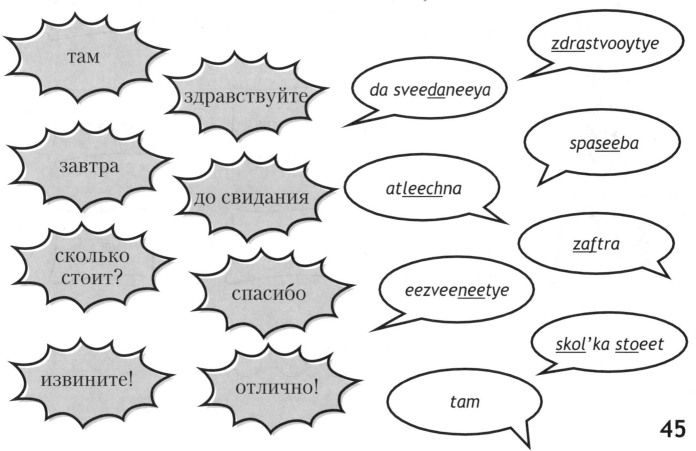

Choose the Russian word that matches the picture to fill in the English word at the bottom of the page.

здесь (p)	нет (c)	да (t)
спасибо (j)	извините! (a)	пожалуйста (l)
да (m)	нет (e)	сегодня (i)
там (b)	здравствуйте (a)	пожалуйста (x)
где? (s)	сегодня (h)	*fchyera* (t)
здравствуйте (b)	нет (y)	да (e)

English word: (p) ( ) ( ) ( ) ( ) ( )

What are these people saying? Write the correct number in each speech bubble, as in the example.

1. здравствуйте   2. пожалуйста   3. да   4. нет

5. здесь   6. извините!   7. где?   8. сколько стоит?

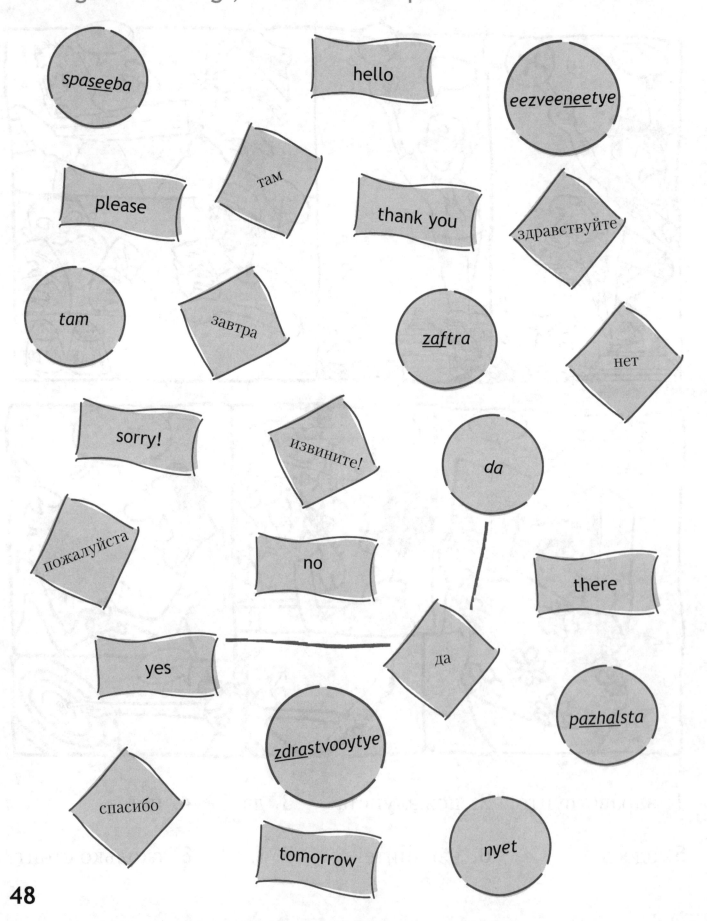

● ROUND-UP

This section is designed to review all the 100 words you have met in the different topics. It is a good idea to test yourself with your flashcards before trying this section.

◎ These ten objects are hidden in the picture. Can you find and circle them?

дверь	цветок	кровать	пальто	шляпа
велосипед	стул	собака	рыба	носок

сегодня

автобус

быстрый

нос

пустыня

да

шкаф

лев

платье

дешёвый

река

нога

50

Find the odd one out in these groups of words and say why.

собака	корова	(стол)	обезьяна

Because it isn't an animal.

- - - - - - - - -

машина	автобус	поезд	телефон

- - - - - - - -

ферма	пальто	рубашка	юбка

- - - - - - -

море	озеро	река	дерево

- - - - - - - -

дорогой	грязный	чистый	кино

- - - - - - - -

кролик	кошка	рыба	лев

- - - - - - - -

рука	софа	голова	живот

- - - - - - - -

пожалуйста	вчера	завтра	сегодня

- - - - - - -

плита	кровать	шкаф	холодильник

◎ **L**ook at the objects below for 30 seconds.

◎ **C**over the picture and try to remember all the objects.
Circle the Russian words for those you remember.

цветок

туфля

спасибо

дверь

кошка

здесь

пальто

поезд

нет

ремень

гора

машина

стул

лошадь

носок

футболка

глаз

кровать

шорты

такси

телевизор

обезьяна

Now match the Russian words, their pronunciation, and the English meanings, as in the example.

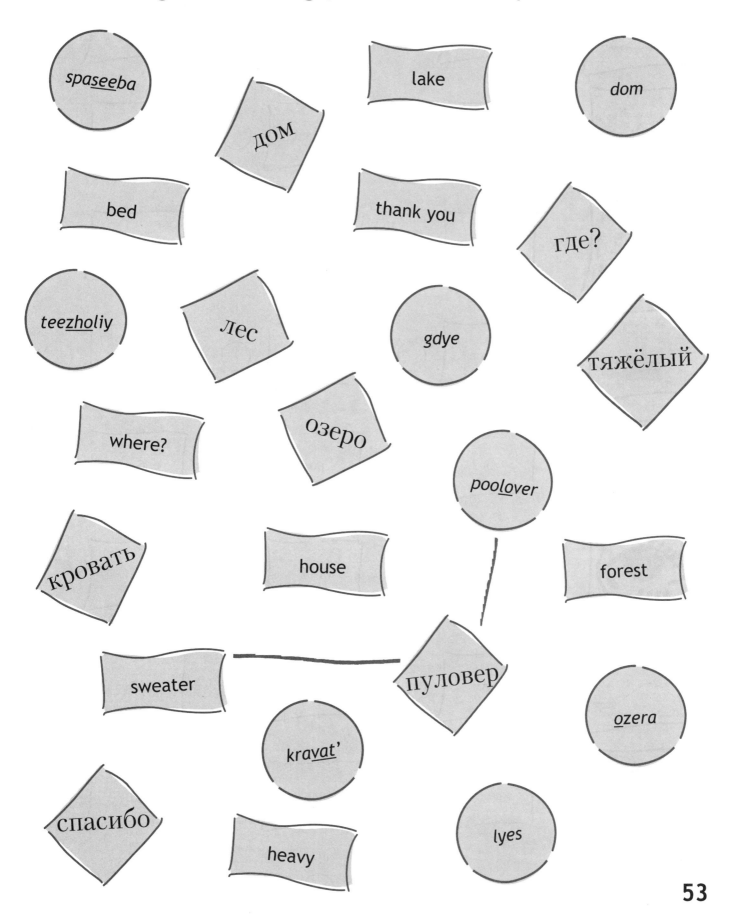

spaseeba

lake

dom

дом

bed

thank you

где?

teezholiy

лес

gdye

тяжёлый

where?

озеро

poolover

кровать

house

forest

sweater

пуловер

ozera

kravat'

спасибо

lyes

heavy

Fill in the English phrase at the bottom of the page.

софа (w)	такси (g)	ухо (t)
пальто (o)	грязный (a)	мост (e)
да (m)	сколько стоит? (l)	сегодня (i)
корова (b)	окно (l)	ресторан (h)
где? (e)	рот (a)	собака (d)
глаз (o)	стол (p)	здравствуйте (v)
холм (n)	нет (y)	автобус (r)
кролик (n)	дорога (e)	плита (s)

English phrase: (w) ( ) ( ) ( )   ( ) ( ) ( ) ( ) !

Look at the two pictures and check (✔) the objects that are different in Picture B.

Picture A

Picture B

шорты	
футболка	
дверь	
кошка	
стул	
рыба	
носок	
собака	

Now join the Russian words to their English equivalents.

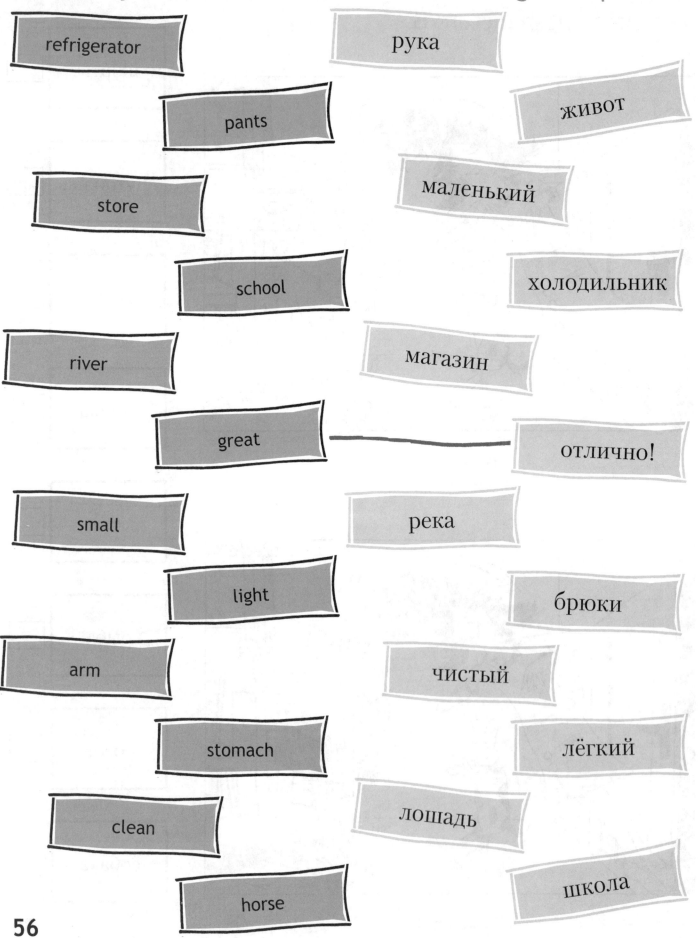

refrigerator

рука

pants

живот

store

маленький

school

холодильник

river

магазин

great —— отлично!

small

река

light

брюки

arm

чистый

stomach

лёгкий

clean

лошадь

horse

школа

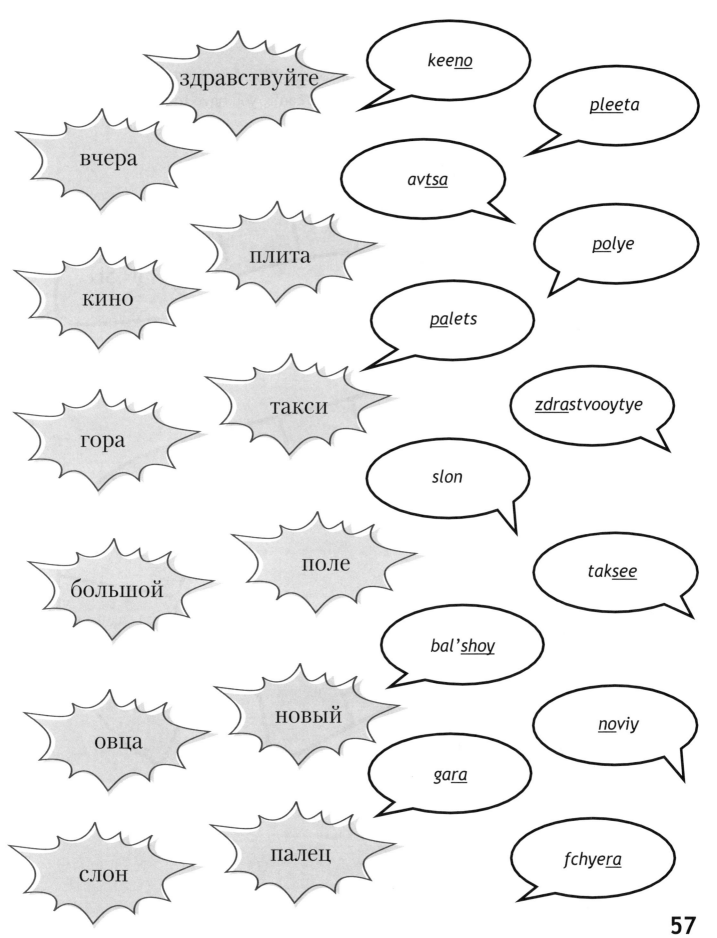

Snake game.

- You will need a die and counter(s). You can challenge yourself to reach the finish or play with someone else. You have to throw the exact number to finish.

- Throw the die and move forward that number of spaces. When you land on a word you must pronounce it and say what it means in English. If you can't, you have to go back to the square you came from.

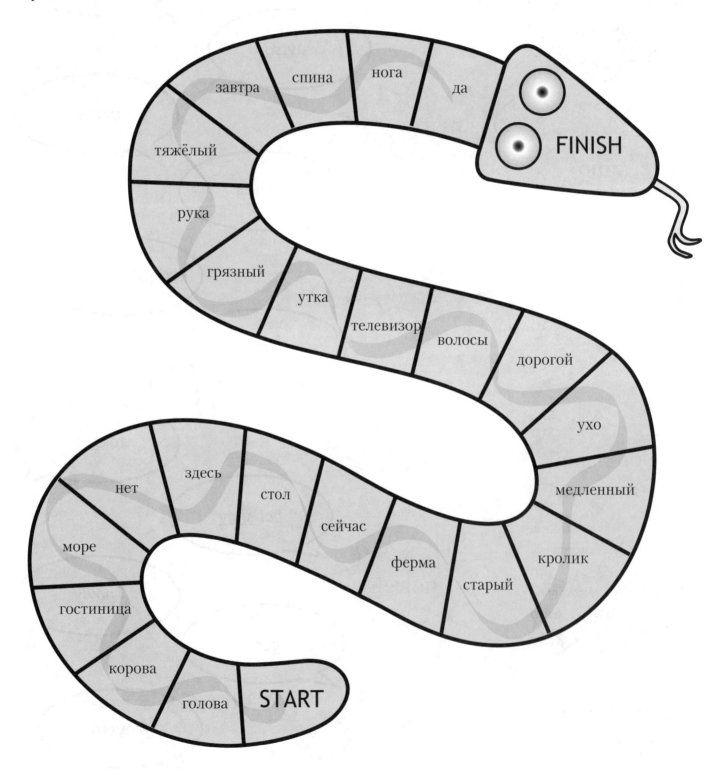

⊚ **A**nswers

❶ Around the home

Page 10 (top)

See page 9 for correct picture.

Page 10 (bottom)

door	дверь
cupboard	шкаф
stove	плита
bed	кровать
table	стол
chair	стул
fridge	холодильник
computer	компьютер

Page 11 (top)

стол	*stol*
шкаф	*shkaf*
компьютер	*kampyooter*
кровать	*kravat'*
окно	*akno*
телефон	*telefon*
телевизор	*televeezar*
стул	*stool*

Page 11 (bottom)

Page 12

Page 13

English word: window

❷ Clothes

Page 15 (top)

платье	*plat'e*
шорты	*shorti*
туфля	*tooflya*
ремень	*remyen'*
рубашка	*roobashka*
футболка	*footbolka*
шляпа	*shlyapa*
носок	*nasok*

Page 15 (bottom)

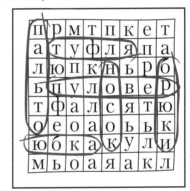

Page 16

hat	шляпа	*shlyapa*
shoe	туфля	*tooflya*
sock	носок	*nasok*
shorts	шорты	*shorti*
T-shirt	футболка	*footbolka*
belt	ремень	*remyen'*
coat	пальто	*pal'to*
trousers	брюки	*bryookee*

Page 17

шляпа (hat)	2
пальто (coat)	0
ремень (belt)	2
туфля (shoe)	2 (1 pair)
брюки (trousers)	0
шорты (shorts)	2
платье (dress)	1
носок (sock)	6 (3 pairs)
юбка (skirt)	1
футболка (t-shirt)	3
рубашка (shirt)	0
пуловер (sweater)	1

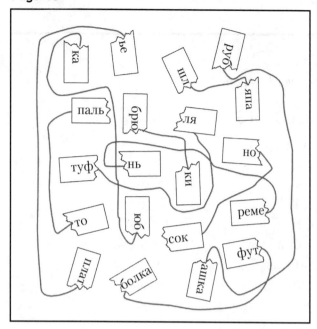

❸ AROUND TOWN

Page 20 (top)

cinema	кино
shop	магазин
hotel	гостиница
taxi	такси
car	машина
train	поезд
school	школа
house	дом

Page 20 (bottom)

bicycle	4
taxi	7
house	2
train	6
bus	1
road	3
car	5

Page 21

школа   такси   автобус

машина   поезд   ресторан

гостиница   велосипед

Page 22

English word: school

Page 23

автобус	*aftoboos*
такси	*taksee*
школа	*shkola*
машина	*masheena*
гостиница	*gasteeneets*
дом	*dom*
велосипед	*vyelaseepyet*
поезд	*poyest*
магазин	*magazeen*
кино	*keeno*
ресторан	*restaran*
дорога	*daroga*

● COUNTRYSIDE

Page 25

See page 24 for correct picture.

Page 26

мост	✔	поле	✔
дерево	✔	лес	✔
пустыня	✘	озеро	✘
холм	✘	река	✔
гора	✔	цветок	✔
море	✘	ферма	✔

Page 27 (top)

гора	*gara*
река	*reka*
лес	*lyes*
пустыня	*poostinya*
море	*morye*
ферма	*ferma*
мост	*most*
поле	*polye*

Page 27 (bottom)

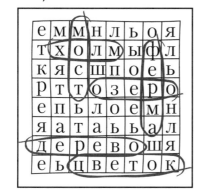

Page 28

sea	море	*morye*
lake	озеро	*ozera*
desert	пустыня	*poostinya*
farm	ферма	*ferma*
flower	цветок	*tsvetok*
mountain	гора	*gara*
river	река	*reka*
field	поле	*polye*

❺ OPPOSITES

Page 30

expensive	дорогой
big	большой
light	лёгкий
slow	медленный
clean	чистый
inexpensive	дешёвый
dirty	грязный
small	маленький
heavy	тяжёлый
new	новый
fast	быстрый
old	старый

Page 31

English word: change

Page 32

Odd one outs are those which are not opposites:

тяжёлый
маленький
новый
грязный
медленный
дешёвый

Page 33

old	новый
big	маленький
new	старый
slow	быстрый
dirty	чистый
small	большой
heavy	лёгкий
clean	грязный
light	тяжёлый
expensive	дешёвый
inexpensive	дорогой

❻ ANIMALS

Page 35

корова　　кролик　　рыба　　　лев

овца　　собака　　обезьяна

лошадь　　мышь　　кошка

Page 36

кролик	*kroleek*
лошадь	*loshat'*
обезьяна	*abes'yana*
собака	*sabaka*
кошка	*koshka*
мышь	*mish'*
утка	*ootka*
рыба	*riba*
лев	*lev*
овца	*avtsa*
корова	*karova*
слон	*slon*

Page 37

elephant	✔	mouse	✘
monkey	✘	cat	✔
sheep	✔	dog	✘
lion	✔	cow	✔
fish	✔	horse	✘
duck	✘	rabbit	✔

Page 38

monkey	обезьяна
cow	корова
mouse	мышь
dog	собака
sheep	овца
fish	рыба
lion	лев
elephant	слон
cat	кошка
duck	утка
rabbit	кролик
horse	лошадь

⑦ PARTS OF THE BODY

Page 40

Page 41 (top)

You should have also drawn pictures of:

leg; mouth; hand/arm; finger; stomach; head

Page 41 (bottom)

голова	*gala<u>va</u>*
ухо	*<u>oo</u>kha*
живот	*zhee<u>vot</u>*
нос	*nos*
рука	*roo<u>ka</u>*
рот	*rot*
глаз	*glas*
спина	*spee<u>na</u>*

Page 42

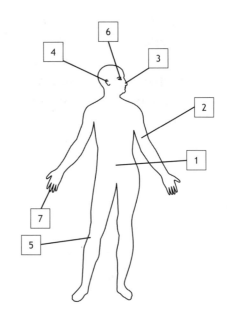

1. живот	*zhee<u>vot</u>*
2. рука	*roo<u>ka</u>*
3. нос	*nos*
4. ухо	*<u>oo</u>kha*
5. нога	*na<u>ga</u>*
6. глаз	*glas*
7. палец	*<u>pa</u>lets*

Page 43

ear	ухо	*<u>oo</u>kha*
hair	волосы	*<u>vo</u>lasi*
hand	рука	*roo<u>ka</u>*
stomach	живот	*zhee<u>vot</u>*
arm	рука	*roo<u>ka</u>*
back	спина	*spee<u>na</u>*
finger	палец	*<u>pa</u>lets*
leg	нога	*na<u>ga</u>*

⑧ USEFUL EXPRESSIONS

Page 45 (top)

great!	отлично!
yes	да
yesterday	вчера
where?	где?
today	сегодня
here	здесь
please	пожалуйста
no	нет

Page 45 (bottom)

там	*tam*
здравствуйте	*zdrastvooytye*
завтра	*zaftra*
до свидания	*da sveedaneeya*
сколько стоит?	*skol'ka stoeet*
спасибо	*spaseeba*
извините!	*eezveeneetye*
отлично!	*atleechna*

Page 46

English word: please

Page 47

Page 48

yes	да	da
hello	здравствуйте	zdrastvooytye
no	нет	nyet
sorry!	извините!	eezveeneetye
please	пожалуйста	pazhalsta
there	там	tam
thank you	спасибо	spaseeba
tomorrow	завтра	zaftra

● ROUND-UP

Page 49

Page 50

= пустыня
= лев
= да
= шкаф
= дешёвый
= сегодня
= река
= нос
= платье
= нога
= быстрый
= автобус

Page 51

стол (Because it isn't an animal.)

телефон (Because it isn't a means of transportation.)

ферма (Because it isn't an item of clothing.)

дерево (Because it isn't connected with water.)

кино (Because it isn't a descriptive word.)

рыба (Because it lives in water/doesn't have legs.)

софа (Because it isn't a part of the body.)

пожалуйста (Because it isn't an expression of time.)

кровать (Because you wouldn't find it in the kitchen.)

Page 52

Words that appear in the picture:

футболка
машина
цветок
туфля
поезд
обезьяна
телевизор
стул
ремень
шорты

Page 53

sweater	пуловер	poolover
lake	озеро	ozera
thank you	спасибо	spaseebaou
bed	кровать	kravat'
house	дом	dom
forest	лес	lyes
where?	где?	gdye
heavy	тяжёлый	teezholiy

Page 54

English phrase: well done!

Page 55

шорты	✔ (shade)
футболка	✘
дверь	✔ (handle)
кошка	✘
стул	✔ (back)
рыба	✔ (direction)
носок	✔ (pattern)
собака	✘

Page 56

fridge	холодильник
trousers	брюки
shop	магазин
school	школаl
river	река
great!	отлично!
small	маленький
light	лёгкий
arm	рука
stomach	живот
clean	чистый
horse	лошадь

Page 57

здравствуйте	zdrastvooytye
вчера	fchyera
плита	pleeta
кино	keeno
такси	taksee
гора	gara
поле	polye
большой	bal'shoy
новый	noviy
овца	avtsa
палец	palets
слон	slon

Page 58

Here are the English equivalents of the words, in order from START to FINISH:

head	galava	ear	ookha
cow	karova	expensive	daragoy
hotel	gasteeneetsa	hair	volasi
sea	morye	television	televeezar
no	nyet	duck	ootka
here	zdyes'	dirty	gryazniy
table	stol	hand	rooka
now	seechas	heavy	teezholiy
farm	ferma	tomorrow	zaftra
old	stariy	back	speena
rabbit	kroleek	leg	naga
slow	myedlenniy	yes	da

компьютер
kampyooter

окно
akno

стол
stol

шкаф
shkaf

холодильник
khaladeel'neek

стул
stool

софа
sofa

плита
pleeta

дверь
dvyer'

кровать
kravat'

телефон
telefon

телевизор
televeezar

window	computer
cupboard	table
chair	fridge
stove	sofa
bed	door
television	telephone

ремень
remyen'

пальто
pal'to

юбка
yoopka

шляпа
shlyapa

футболка
footbolka

туфля
tooflya

пуловер
poolover

рубашка
roobashka

шорты
shorti

носок
nasok

брюки
bryookee

платье
plat'e

coat	belt
hat	skirt
shoe	t-shirt
shirt	sweater
sock	shorts
dress	trousers

школа

shkola

машина

masheena

дорога

daroga

кино

keeno

гостиница

gasteeneetsa

магазин

magazeen

такси

taksee

велосипед

vyelaseepyet

ресторан

restaran

автобус

aftoboos

поезд

poyest

дом

dom

car	school
cinema	road
shop	hotel
bicycle	taxi
bus	restaurant
house	train

озеро

ozera

лес

lyes

холм

kholm

море

morye

гора

gara

дерево

dyereva

пустыня

poostinya

цветок

tsvetok

мост

most

река

reka

ферма

ferma

поле

polye

forest	lake
sea	hill
tree	mountain
flower	desert
river	bridge
field	farm

тяжёлый

teezholiy

лёгкий

lyokhkeey

большой

bal'shoy

маленький

malyen'keey

старый

stariy

новый

noviy

быстрый

bistriy

медленный

myedlenniy

чистый

cheestiy

грязный

gryazniy

дешёвый

deshoviy

дорогой

daragoy

light	heavy
small	big
new	old
slow	fast
dirty	clean
expensive	cheap

утка
ootka

кошка
koshka

мышь
mish'

корова
karova

кролик
kroleek

собака
sabaka

лошадь
loshat'

обезьяна
abes'yana

лев
lev

рыба
riba

слон
slon

овца
avtsa

cat	duck
cow	mouse
dog	rabbit
monkey	horse
fish	lion
sheep	elephant